I'm Here to Help

A Hospice Worker's Guide to Communicating With Dying People and Their Loved Ones

M. Catherine Ray

I wish to acknowledge the many people in my workshops
whose experiences and stories contributed to these pages.
Additionally, I'm grateful to the members of my own
hospice program at Methodist, and especially to the
people who have permitted me to play a part in their
personal dying and bereavement.

First printing November 1992
Second printing March 1993
Third printing June 1993
Fourth printing February 1994
Fifth printing April 1994
Sixth printing September 1994
Seventh printing February 1995
Eighth printing May 1995
Ninth printing October 1995
Tenth printing January 1996

ISBN 0-963611-0-1

Preface

Not long ago, a close friend called me from work. She is a Personnel Supervisor and she described an unusual dilemma.

"This employee, 'Larry,' has worked here for years and now he's dying of cancer. Friday's his last day, so we're having a party for him. His manager asked what he wanted written on his cake, and Larry told him, 'Enjoy yourself — and with an exclamation mark.' Now I'm supposed to order this cake, and the place is all in an uproar. People say his manager must have misunderstood what Larry said — but they're too embarrassed to ask him again. I personally don't see what's so strange about it, but I finally told them I knew someone who worked with hospices, and I'd get an outside opinion. What do you think about all this?"

My friend didn't know if Larry was in hospice. But he certainly embodied the hospice philosophy: he focused on living while respecting his dying as a normal, natural transition. I only hope his managers get the message.

I have faith that they will. The hospice philosophy spreads with each family it touches. Small wonder that the number of hospice programs has more than doubled in my home state of Minnesota since presenting my first hospice workshop, in 1985. Hospice makes a difference; nationwide statistics prove it as much as the personal stories one hears.

I'm Here to Help was written for the people who are responsible for that growth — the hospice volunteers and professionals who, on any given day, are helping thousands of families live with dying.

Such people are among the most life-loving humans I know. They are nondefensive, sensitive — a disproportionate percentage of 'feeling types' is drawn to this work. Hospice workers are plateaus beyond initial fears and embarrassments; they are comfortable with life's complexities. They share a healthy acceptance of death and dying, and most have superb senses of humor.

They are often asked "why they do what they do," by skeptical friends and family.

The answer is simple: hospice workers get to eat cake with people like Larry.

Enjoy yourself!

About This Book

I'm Here to Help is a book for hospice workers — volunteers and professionals alike — anyone on the team who communicates with dying people and their loved ones. The tips and techniques covered have been evolving since my first hospice workshop in 1985. Since then, I've presented many more seminars, become a hospice volunteer, and most important, experienced the loss of loved ones. I decided to compile the information I've collected... to offer a written version of what's in my head and in my workshops.

I didn't see the need to replicate the wonderful books and essays I've read which discuss hospice philosophy, death, dying and bereavement. Instead, I wanted to provide something I hadn't read... a handbook of those specific communication skills necessary in hospice, backed by interpersonal communication principles, models, and theory.

Therefore, *I'm Here to Help* is intentionally succinct... as practical and concentrated a presentation as possible, given the complexity of the subject matter. I use a short 'pointer' format, intending to be both 'hands on' and reader-friendly. There are few extended examples or explanations. The Table of Contents is detailed, so readers can more easily skim the book for their personal areas of interest.

I hope that new volunteers will read this book during training. I hope that seasoned volunteers and professionals will use *I'm Here to Help* for an occasional refresher. In short, I wish to expand the audience beyond those hospice workers I meet in my training classes.

Readers of this book are undoubtedly similar to the people in my workshops — you already intuitively know and practice much of what I'm about to present. You also have ideas to add; in fact, several pointers in this book originated from workshop participants. Hopefully, *I'm Here to Help* consolidates what you already experience, offers new ideas, and also provides an avenue for sharing your own skills and strategies.

Table of Contents

Helping People Open Up To You

Listening, Feedback, and Managing Conversations

Nonverbal Techniques

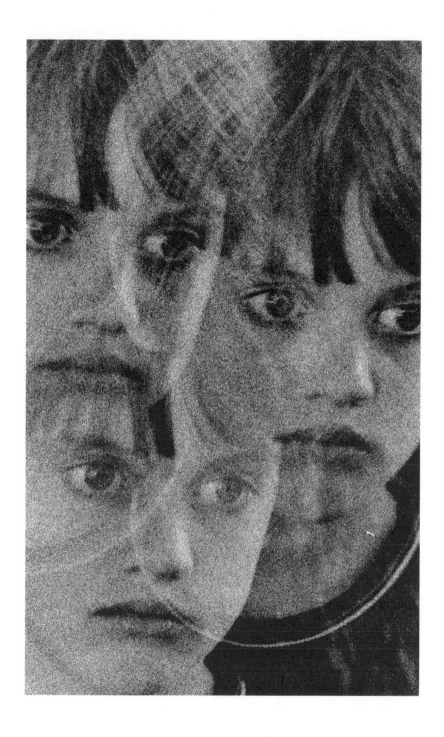

Philosophical and Spiritual Approaches

• **Avoid offering definitions of death, the 'hereafter,'** etc.
However, encourage the other person to define this experience,
spiritually or otherwise, with no argument from you.

• **Try not to 'deny the reality' of somebody else...** such as saying
to them, "Oh, come on now, you can't really mean that!"

• **Remember that the famous 'Five Stages of Death' are
ever-changing.**

Denial —> Anger —> Bargaining —> Depression —> Acceptance

No one ever goes through this process entirely predictably or
completely chronologically.

• Just as s/he changes **physically** — and sometimes drastically — week to week, your patient also changes **spiritually** and **philosophically**. You do not see the 'same' person today that you saw 4 days ago.

• **These philosophical and spiritual changes occur in loved ones, too.**

• **Remember that each friend and family member has a unique relationship,** and carries a unique perspective regarding the dying loved one.

• **Do not attempt to 'share' someone's grief,** and be wary of overdoing the empathy. People get very protective and possessive of their grief.

• **Accept human diversity:**
  – **Culture determines what is appropriate interpersonal behavior...** for instance, Native Americans may avoid eye contact as a sign of respect, and an Anglo American might label those averted eyes as 'unassertive' or even 'deceitful.' A reserved European American might seem 'closed' or 'controlling' to a more expressive, confrontational African American. Be wary of stereotyping.
  – **Personality preferences play a part...** you might find it energizing to be around others while s/he needs solitude to 'restore the batteries.' She might be more 'logical' while he might be more 'emotional.' You prefer a set agenda while he operates more spontaneously (See Keirsey and Bates, *Please Understand Me*).
  – **Communication styles will differ...** you have a 'fight' approach while he prefers to 'take flight' ("Let's just get the cards on the table" vs. "Can't we just sleep on it and try to have a good time tonight?"). He is quite expressive nonverbally, and physically demonstrative; she is reserved and prefers to keep her distance. [Important note: Often these people are married. Happily.]

- **Become tolerant,** if not even comfortable and enthusiastic, about a wide range of rituals/beliefs surrounding life, death, and the dying process.

- In a world plagued by AIDS, hospice caregivers must **examine our own philosophies** regarding sexuality and drug abuse. Do we have religious/spiritual foundations that might pose a barrier?

- **In no way impose your own values, attitudes and beliefs onto this family.** Are there areas/issues where you might feel judgmental?

- **Broaden your experience by exploring other cultures** and their definitions of death and dying. Read, talk to people of different faiths and nations, and attend their ceremonies.

NOTES

Boundaries

- **Set boundaries.** Observe the suffering and remain compassionate, but don't immerse yourself.

- **Avoid thinking you can solve other peoples' problems.**

- **Be on the lookout for client/family dependency on you.**

- **Learn to say "No."**

- **Be aware of your own 'unfinished business'...** the things you think and feel about dying, and why... your own experience with death and dying could negatively affect your work with the family if you aren't careful.

• **Remember that 'unfinished business' goes beyond one's perspective on dying...** for example, imagine that your patient's husband is alcoholic and <u>you</u> grew up in an alcoholic family... take care that your own experience with chemical dependency doesn't negatively affect your work with the family.

• **Avoid becoming the family's therapist.** Are you being pulled in, in ways that feel uncomfortable? Tactfully tell them so.

• **Try not to turn your own family and friends into <u>your</u> therapists** (for ways to avoid this, see "Taking Care of Yourself," pages 61-62).

• **I know I'm exceeding my boundaries when:**

— I lose objectivity... for instance, I become resentful toward a family member (even if I don't openly express it)

— My stress increases... I feel emotionally on edge with my own family and friends

— I find myself thinking about the patient/loved ones too frequently

— I feel like I want to take over

— I feel like the patient is **my** responsibility.

NOTES

Family Systems

- **The most important people in a person's life are also that person's biggest frustration.** (We are often hardest on those who love us most... we trust them not to abandon us, even if we aren't always polite or nice.)

- **It is true that 'opposites attract.'** (This can be a major source of those frustrations.)

- **Continue to learn about family systems and interpersonal communications.** Read books on these subjects (available in the psychology or self-help section of any major bookstore... an even better resource is a textbook in these subjects, available at most college bookstores... these textbooks are quite 'reader-friendly' and packed with information).

- **Accept the family, 'wherever they are'** in dealing with this experience... which will change day-to-day (from 'fighting it' to 'accepting it' and everything in between).

- Fortunately or unfortunately, **individual family members are rarely at the same collective 'place'** in this process.

- **Each family member brings a unique perspective and plateau** to this experience; each has a unique relationship with the dying person.

- **Watch out for triangle traps...** do not get 'hooked' between spouses, siblings, between parents and children, etc.

- **People have problems above and beyond their illness...** kids continue to have trouble at school, cars still break down... the little day-to-day irritations of life don't stop when a person has an incurable illness. Instead, they just compound the pressure.

- **Families also have major problems...** such as financial troubles, chemical dependency, damaged relationships. The functional problems that existed in this family prior to the illness are still there... and may even be exacerbated. Do not think these problems can be solved... deathbed reconciliations do occur, but try to leave romantic illusions at the theatre.

- **Families have distinct rules** — even though they probably have not been discussed or formalized — about which feelings/ideas can be expressed. You can tell what things are 'okay' to express by watching various family members as they interact with one another.

- **Families have distinct communication styles.** Just because a family is very loud and argumentative doesn't mean they are unhappy or ready to separate. Just because a family is very reserved and unaffectionate doesn't mean they are uncaring or 'stuffing feelings.'

- **Our own family history alters our perceptions of the families we work with...** again, we must be wary of our own 'unfinished business.'

- **A major comfort of the hospice worker is the <u>consistency</u> s/he offers** to the family, in a time of great upheaval. Take care to support family routines... rules... roles... avoid interrupting family patterns (even if you disagree with them).

NOTES

Giving The Family 'Control'

- **When a family joins hospice they are 'bombarded' with new names and relationships…** social workers, nurses, clergy, home health aides, volunteers… make it easier for them by wearing a name tag, providing schedule consistency whenever possible, and calling first to confirm visits.

- **Give each and every family member maximum information,** and do not be discouraged or disgruntled when you find your **information has to be repeated or clarified.** People in this situation have difficulty 'hearing' because they are already dealing with so much that is new and uncertain. And it is normal that one family member will confuse or distort something you said, when s/he repeats it to someone else.

- **Encourage the family in its efforts to educate itself** about the illness and the dying process. Try to be a resource of people, books, and helpful ideas (without 'soapboxing').

- **Encourage the family to make as many decisions as possible...** for instance, rather than suggesting a menu or scheduling appointments, allow the family to experiment to see which food items work, or how their days are most comfortably organized.

- **When the family is 'stuck' on a problem, teach them brainstorming** techniques, next help them learn to **prioritize** the most workable ideas... then **step back,** out of the process. Avoid judging the family's perceptions of problems or their solutions.

- **Encourage the family to try something new for a brief time...** then help them know that it is okay to change directions. For instance, the family needs to rearrange living space or alter a diet... "Let's try this for a few days. If it doesn't work, we'll figure out something new to try."

- **Give family members active and direct permission about 'losing control'** emotionally. Keep tissues handy and don't be shy about handing them out. Affirm emotional reactions directly, saying things like, "It's okay to cry. If I were in your shoes, I'd be crying too." **At a different time,** remind the person how much s/he is accomplishing. (If you compliment them then, they will think you are merely placating them or trying to make them stop being so 'emotional.')

- **Learn stress management techniques and when appropriate 'teach' them** to the family so they can better help themselves when team members are not present.

- **People often feel more powerful/in control when they are actively 'doing something'** about a problem. Do not discourage the family from trying to 'do things,' even if you feel their actions are futile or silly.

NOTES

Helping People Open Up To You

- **Believe** what your patient/client family members tell you...
  about pain management, coping mechanisms, etc. Do not discount
  their perceptions or experiences, even mildly.

- Hospice social workers find that major emotional complaints of
  patients are 'isolation' and 'boredom.' **The hospice worker can
  become a vital companion.**

- **Do not say "I know how you feel."** This is <u>not</u> empathy. This is
  merely presumptuous.

- **Watch out for the trap, "What would <u>you</u> do?"** Often, people
  will ask for your advice, and not because they really want it, but
  because it provides them with an opening to talk about THEIR
  problems. So, instead of answering their question in detail, turn the
  conversation back to them as quickly as possible. Say something
  like, "Well, for me, it was like this but I know every family is
  different. What's going on in <u>your</u> situation?"

- **Avoid overdoing descriptions of your own experience...** otherwise, you will unintentionally monopolize the 'airtime.'

- **Respect the family's wishes to use euphemisms;** for example, calling incurable lung cancer "my problem." Adjust your language accordingly.

- **Be comfortable as an 'initiator.'** Practice various methods until you can initiate 'difficult' topics with assertive sensitivity.

- **Some initiating techniques are:**

  "Can You Tell Me?"   "Can you tell me how your daughter made these cookies?"

  The Honest (and not overdone) Compliment   "That robe is such a beautiful color — it really brings out the blue in your eyes."

  The Whimsical Hook-In   "So, what would <u>you</u> name a planet if you discovered it?"

  Mutual Interests   "Did you refinish that table yourself? I'm working on a chest of drawers..."

  External Events   "What did you think of that article in the paper this morning?"

  The 'Here and Now' Environment   "This room sure gets a lot of sun, doesn't it?"

- If the previous examples seem too commonplace or 'boring,' just remember... **'big talk' usually starts with 'small talk.'**

- **Avoid feeling frustrated or impatient with 'the same old conversations' about the weather, sports, etc.** Such talk (known as phatic communication) provides a vital trust-building function.

- **When initiating 'difficult' topics,** the two rules are:
  1. **Ask permission** to talk about the topic
  2. **Give the person an 'out' at your own expense,** rather than his/hers

  For example, say "Can I ask a personal question, or am I being a bit too nosey" rather than, "Is it okay to talk about this, or is it just too painful for you?"

- **Use specific and direct initiation questions,** rather than an ambiguous 'nicety.' For example, ask "How did your son react when he found out about your illness?" rather than saying, "If you ever want to talk about anything, just let me know."

- **Do not be too shy to ask 'scary' questions** such as "Are you afraid?" or "What does it feel like to know death is near?" Many patients are grateful for the opportunity to verbalize things that they may withhold from the loved ones they want to 'protect.'

- A good way to help the patient talk is to **ask about prized possessions, collections, evidence of hobbies,** etc.

- **Asking to look at photo albums** is another good technique; it can lead to a visit rich with stories, as the patient reviews and celebrates a lifetime of experience and memories.

- If asking to look at photos of family members feels too 'forward' or 'pushy,' try asking to look at **pictures of objects the patient has mentioned...** "Do you have any pictures of that cabin you built?"... "Did you ever take any pictures of your garden?"... These photos will likely lead to others.

- **Sharing 'stories' is a wonderful tool for gaining trust...** telling a <u>quick</u> story about yourself will help open the door, but remember that your objective is to hear about <u>them</u>. Use <u>your</u> stories as a method for evoking <u>theirs</u>.

- **Ask for stories.** "Tell me how you and your husband met." "How did you get started in your career?"

- **'Talking' is no measure of intimacy.** The closest and most comfortable relationships are ones where we can be together in total silence.

- As the patient approaches death, she sleeps a lot and turns inward, gathering spiritual energy for this important transition. She **expends less energy in here-and-now conversations and interpersonal relationships.** During these quiet times, you can help most by remaining silent, making her comfortable, and holding her hand, stroking her head, etc. (showing her that you are nearby).

- **This sleeping and turning inward can be especially difficult for loved ones...** they may remember an active, vibrant person who was always 'the life of the party.' Family members might complain or worry about the patient's 'quality of life.' Try to help them understand that the patient is 'active' and indeed his/her life may be taking on a 'quality' more intense than ever... it's just that we can't 'see' it in the ways we did before.

- **The patient may use symbolic language** or speak in ways which seem confusing to caretakers... often the caretakers may say "she's rambling."

- This **incoherent 'mind-wandering' talk is packed with information,** if we listen carefully. The patient may be using metaphors and other symbolic language to communicate two major things: first, what it feels like to die and second, what s/he needs to make a peaceful exit. (See Final Gifts by Callanan and Kelley.)

- **Listen metaphorically and symbolically** — not just literally (see next section on Listening).

- **The patient and caretakers do not need to be 'entertained' or 'distracted'** with anecdotes or jokes, etc. Such talk can be trivializing and offensive.

- **It can be really depressing to be with someone who <u>insists</u> on cheering you up.** It takes <u>so</u> much effort to 'be happy' for someone, when really we'd rather wallow for a while.

- **Remember that some feelings are more socially acceptable than others.** For instance, feeling 'anger' is more acceptable than 'fear' in our society. Thus, some expressed feelings could be surface, masking the <u>real</u> emotions. Someone who seems very angry could be even more scared and sad.

- **Some people view their world more 'logically' and others view their world more 'emotionally.'** (See *Please Understand Me* by Keirsey and Bates.) In general, it is best to operate within <u>their</u> framework rather than your own. If you are warm/fuzzy/touchy/ feely with an analytical person, you'll drive her crazy. If you are all 'head' with a 'heart' person, he'll view you as cold and aloof.

- **<u>Occasionally</u>, it can be helpful to gently break out of the 'head' and 'heart' mode.** If someone typically expresses what she <u>thinks</u>, ask also how she feels. When someone expresses <u>feelings</u>, ask also for his thoughts.

- **Sometimes, the very words 'thoughts' or 'feelings' can be threatening.** In situations where you decide not to be so direct, use a more neutral question… "What was your response to that?" or "How did you react then?"

- **Many patients will confide in a hospice worker things they would never say to a family member or friend…** there is a deep comfort in this short term relationship, which began with two virtual strangers and no 'history' or preconceived notions.

- At the end of the dying process, many patients have dreams, visions of loved ones who have died, and feelings that they will die soon. Often, patients are afraid to tell their families and friends about these profound experiences because "It will frighten them, or they'll think I'm hallucinating, they'll put me in a nursing home." **Hospice workers are often rewarded with hearing these stories.**

- **It is essential for the hospice worker to become a supportive, ethical confidante.** Build trust, acceptance, and know when to keep a secret.

NOTES

Listening, Feedback and Managing Conversations

- It's been said before, and for good reason... **listening is the single most important thing we do.** We must listen well to each family member, and we must listen to each member of the hospice team.

- **Listen with <u>all</u> five senses**... humans can gather powerful information in every interaction, especially when they pay attention to sight, smell, touch, taste... in addition to sound.

- **Listen for literal information, but also listen figuratively.** Patients and caregivers often express themselves through symbols and metaphors... their communication is not always direct or explicit (see Callanan and Kelley, *Final Gifts*).

- **'Labels'** we give to other people ('bureaucrat,' 'yuppie,' 'old maid,' etc.) get in the way of our listening to them.

- **Few 'labels' are more emotionally charged than this one: 'Dying Person.'** By the time you meet them, this label has already altered or eliminated many of the family's former friendships.

- **'Loaded' language will also get in the way** of open listening. A 'loaded' word is anything which carries a powerful emotional punch, such as "chick," "imbecile," "fag." Unfortunately, they are different for everybody, so you might use one unintentionally. (Example, "Oh, God!") Take care to choose words which are as 'value-neutral' as possible.

- **Watch out for 'naughty' words** — they evoke defensiveness:

You/Your   **"You** didn't call me back to tell me whether I should pick up **your** father's prescription." Instead try: "I was concerned because I wanted to plan for my visit."

Always   Your son **always** forgets to call me back." Instead, say: "Many times, I haven't received a call back from Larry."

Never   "She **never** writes out her instructions so I can read them." Instead: "It seems like I have a hard time reading these instructions, too much of the time."

Why   **"Why** do **you** feel that way?" Instead try: "I wonder what brings about those feelings?

Should   "**You** really **should** talk to a lawyer about revising **your** will." Try instead: "Some people find it helpful to talk to their lawyers about these kind of concerns."

- **The word YOU evokes <u>ego</u>.** Get the ego (you) out of any message which is **correcting…** "I was hoping for a return to my phone call." But keep the ego (you) <u>in</u> when **complimenting…** "You have the prettiest smile!"

- **Avoid changing the subject.** Let the <u>other</u> person do that.

- **Listening occurs at five different levels,** each requiring greater energy and involvement. It's like walking up steps… the higher you climb, the greater your energy and involvement.

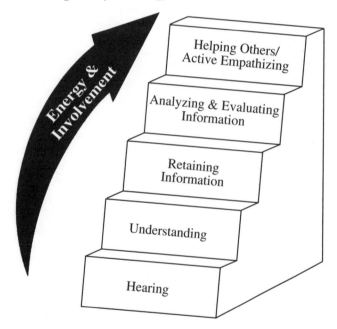

- **Most hospice workers will be required to listen at the Top Level,** using active empathy and sometimes even counseling skills. This is hard work!

- **Top Level listening is a lot of work**, because you have to hold in your opinions. At this level, you are restricted to using **only Nonevaluative Feedback techniques** (see Seven Methods for Giving Nonevaluative Feedback, page 37).

- **Nonevaluative Feedback means holding back your <u>negative</u> judgments** ("That doesn't sound like it will work!"). It also means **holding back your <u>favorable</u> opinions** ("What a great idea!"). Why hold back our positive feedback, you ask? Because it keeps the person too focused on that one 'good' idea and hinders her in exploring other options/thoughts/feelings.

- **Feedback does more than 'respond'... it actually <u>changes</u> the messages to follow.** If our feedback judges or evaluates what was said, the speaker will feel compelled to change the message, or perhaps stop talking prematurely. If our feedback is free of evaluation or judgment, we encourage the person to communicate more freely and fully. For example, imagine a conversation with a primary caregiver:

  SHE: "I'm just so tired, I think I'll explode."

  YOU: "That's such a normal feeling, and nothing to feel guilty about. Perhaps we can arrange some respite care."

  — or —

  YOU: "I see. Tell me more about it."

  Both responses are good ones, but which one allows the caregiver to solve her own problems (and gives her more control)? Sometimes, counseling communicators mistakenly try to solve other peoples' problems too quickly, before they have had a chance to discuss and solve their problems for themselves.

- **It is important to note that Nonevaluative Feedback requires more energy and <u>much</u> more time.** In that last example, for instance, it would be harder to say, "Tell me more" if the caregiver made the comment at the end of your visit (and your son was waiting for you to pick him up at soccer practice). Do not feel guilty when you make the decision to refrain from giving nonevaluative feedback.

- **The quickest way to stop a conversation is to provide advice, opinions, evaluations.**

• **Seven methods for giving Nonevaluative Feedback:**

**Minimal
Encouragers:**
Soft murmurs, "Um hm," to acknowledge what is said, while taking little 'air time.'

Probing:
Ask for more information. "What was your response when he reacted that way?"

Acknowledging:
Comment on the behavior of the other in a neutral manner. "I hear some frustration in your voice when you talk about that situation." (NOTE: You are not saying, "I agree. I would be frustrated, too, in that situation.")

Checking Out:
Repeat, clarify, reflect, paraphrase. "You say you are confused because this is the fourth time they've changed her prescription?"

Paraphrase:
Use different words than the ones the speaker chose, and re-state what you heard. This will help you both to clarify underlying values, hidden attitudes, or unverbalized assumptions. "So, you were feeling angry, or maybe hurt, because he didn't appear concerned?"

Repetition:
Use the same words the speaker chose, and repeat verbatim what you heard. This will help you both to clarify specific terms, tangible 'contract' issues, and verify the accuracy of statements. "So, her specific words were, 'in ten days to two weeks,' is that right?'

Summarizing:
A combination of all the techniques except 'probing,' in which you pull together the main ideas you heard in a concise paragraph or two. This is a very useful closure technique; it marks the end of your nonevaluative feedback time and helps the person move into 'evaluating' the situation. After your summary statements, you can help the person generate solutions/make decisions.

- **Three rules for giving Nonevaluative Feedback:**

  1. **Remember that giving nonevaluative feedback is very tiring.** It is hard to hold back our opinions; this strategy requires tremendous self-discipline and a lot of time.

  2. **Sometimes we evaluate, even when we don't intend to.** Usually, this happens through our tone of voice rather than the words we use. For example, practice all the ways you could say a simple, "Um hmm."

      > "Um HMMM…" (surprise)
      > "Um Hmmmm…" (skepticism)
      > "UM Hmmm…" (agreement)
      > "Um Hm…" (sarcasm)

  3. **The person receiving Nonevaluative Feedback will feel 'validated,' and will often believe you AGREE with what you are hearing.** This can be dangerous! "But you <u>said</u> you thought my mother was wrong… well, you certainly never <u>disagreed</u> with me!?!"

- **'Acceptance' is <u>not</u> 'agreement.'**

- **Monitor the airtime.** Hopefully, <u>you</u> aren't using much of it.

- **Again, keeping our responses judgment-free requires tremendous attention and self-discipline.**

- **Accept the fact that sometimes you won't have the energy to 'climb the stairs' to Top Level listening.** Do not apologize, but do explain: "Marge, I'm distracted right now by outside stuff, but this sounds important…" **When you postpone an important conversation, set a <u>specific</u> time to hold it at a later date;** e.g., "Can we talk about this later?" is not as effective as "Could I come over for coffee tomorrow at 7:30?"

- **'Uptones' and 'Downtones' are a vocalization technique** which can reduce defensiveness and manage conversational flow. If the last syllable of your sentence goes up in tone, you sound like you are asking a question. If the last syllable goes down in tone, you sound like you are making a statement. For example, say each of these sentences twice, once with an uptone and once with a downtone:

    "Would you mind if I came on Friday, next week?"

    "The doctor wants to limit your mother's visitors to immediate family."

  You should be able to hear distinct differences. An 'uptone' sounds tentative, approachable and inviting. A 'downtone' sounds decisive, powerful, and conclusive.

- **Use 'uptones' when you want to:**
    — encourage someone to keep talking
    — soften the blow of bad news
    — make a statement sound like a question

- **Use 'downtones' when you want to:**
    — conclude a conversation
    — predetermine the response to a specific question
    — make a question sound like a statement

- **Another time-management technique exists in choosing close-ended or open-ended questions.** A close-ended question elicits yes or no, or other short answers, and does not foster further communication.

    Close-ended: "What time is your appointment?"

    "Ten thirty."

  An open-ended question has no predetermined response and allows the respondent to elaborate.

    Open-ended: "What happened when the nurse came by?"
    or

    "What happened when your daughter told the grandkids?"

- **Use open-ended questions when you want to:**
  - — encourage the client/loved one to talk
  - — get more information and insight from the client/loved one
  - — help the family explore values, problems, possible solutions

- **Use close-ended questions when:**
  - — you want to obtain concise, specific information from the client
  - — you want to get the client back 'on track,' conversationally
  - — you want to begin the ritual of ending the visit/conversation
  - — you sense yourself and/or the client beginning to tire

- **Hospice workers avoid giving advice,** refrain from judging reactions or decisions, and let patients and loved ones work through the process of dying for themselves.

- **Hospice workers learn to become comfortable with awkward pauses and long periods of quiet...** this is especially true toward the end, when the patient turns inward and rests a lot, in preparation for the final departure.

- **Strive to understand,** rather than striving to be understood.

- **Your biggest gift is frequently your silence.**

NOTES

Nonverbal Techniques

- Pay careful attention to the **environment** — 'special' furniture, traffic patterns, privacy issues, etc. Place this family in the context of their surroundings… you can gain a lot of information by observing (and respecting) how they use their belongings/surroundings to define themselves. Are doors open/closed? Is there a cluttered/austere appearance? Are conversation areas public/intimate? Respect the family's choices.

- **How we use and define time** is a nonverbal element — the glance at the watch during a conversation, the meeting held at 7:30 vs. the one at noon — these things are not vocal, but they do shape the interaction.

- **Time is power.** In any relationship, the person who controls the clock has more power. In a job interview, the potential employer can be 'late'; not so the applicant. It is the parent, not the child, who determines how family time is spent (bedtimes, vacation days, doctor's appointments, etc.). It is the boss who determines the time for the meeting, not the employee.

- **Dying people and their loved ones have lost control of the clock.** One moment, they lived with the idea that their futures were more or less infinite... the next moment, they came home from the doctor with parameters. This can make people feel powerless.

- **Persons who are not primary caregivers may unintentionally abuse the family's time.** Such people often want to spend time with the patient for their own purposes; they may not realize that the dying person has little energy for interpersonal relationships, especially as death approaches. Hospice workers can help educate the family to set limits, and they can spread the word that a ten minute visit might be ample.

- We help the family when we **allow them to decide how they spend their time** — being flexible to changing plans, not taking it personally when people prefer not to interact with us.

- **Touch the client often and appropriately**... with permission. People with incurable illnesses are not touched as frequently as they were before; we are nervous about hurting them, or worse, disease can carry a stigma. Brush the client's hair, massage his hands, hug her, stroke his arm.

- **Touch is cultural;** some cultures are 'huggers' while some prefer to keep their distance. Be sensitive... avoid overwhelming the family with your affections.

- **Be aware of the potential 'power trip' in touching someone.** In any relationship, the person with more power touches the other person more often. Teachers pat their students' shoulders with familiarity — the student would never be so 'disrespectful' as to return this gesture. The manager congratulates the employee with a hearty pat on the back — but if the employee did this to the boss, s/he would be considered 'forward.' The hospice worker can overdo a good thing, if her touching becomes intrusive.

- **Eye contact can also be 'too much of a good thing.'** First, eye contact is culturally determined; some cultures view it as a sign of disrespect. Second, just about everybody needs some private time when face-to-face in conversation. Look away occasionally as the person gathers his thoughts or deals with a complex emotion.

- **Height is power.** Get your head lower than the client's. Use a short stool, sit on the floor beside the couch, lean forward in your chair. Position your face so that you are looking up at the client, rather than down on her. Nurses, though much of their work is performed above the client, can still find 60 seconds or so to crouch by the bed for some gentle conversation.

- **Your chin is the most powerful part of your body.** When your chin is in the air, you are 'looking down your nose' at someone. You appear superior, condescending, or confrontational. (Try it in the mirror and see.) To give the family more power, ever-so-slightly drop your chin to your chest in each interaction.

- **People who 'take up a lot of space' are more powerful...** big gestures, wide movements, arms akimbo or on hips. You'll empower the family if you tone down your gestures and keep your arms closer to your sides.

- **A pen is a power symbol...** a reflection back to those days when our parents shook their fingers at us... any sort of 'pointer' or 'extension' held in the hands (such as glasses) operates as a symbol of authority. Hold the pen when you go for a bank loan... put it in your pocket when talking to patients and loved ones.

- **The voice determines power...** your tone, rate, volume, vocal variety, diction... all can intimidate or invite. A tentative, softer tone can be more calming than strong tones with a lot of vocal variety. However, if you sound 'sickeningly sweet' to a patient/loved one with a confrontational style, you'll drive him crazy.

- **'Mirror' the other person.** Match her voice, posture, gestures. Adapt to <u>her</u> nonverbal style and preferences to create extra empathy and trust.

- **Learn how to read 'deceit'...** and yes, the eyes <u>do</u> lie. We are very adept at masking our eyes and facial expressions to pretend that "everything is just fine." We are <u>not</u> so adept at remembering to control other parts of our body... we might jiggle our feet or curl our toes, we might pull on our nose or cover our mouth when telling a falsehood.

- **If a person's vocal message contradicts her nonverbal behavior, we believe the nonverbal portion...** for example, the caretaker looks down and sighs as she tells you that her career isn't suffering.

- **How we touch ourselves is a good clue to our <u>real</u> inner state.** Such self-touches are 'out of awareness'... we don't really realize that we are doing it... and therefore observing these touches can be very helpful for finding the person behind the mask. There are three main types:

  Soothing Self-Touch: Where I stroke my arm, hands, hug myself, or touch myself in other comforting ways when I talk. **Used when** I want to calm myself, tell myself that things will be all right.

  Stimulating Self-Touch: Where I touch myself in more erotic but not 'taboo' places... stroking my own neck, thigh or lips as I speak. **Used when** I feel alert, happy, involved in the conversation.

Punishing Self-Touch: If I exaggerated this self-touch, I would inflict pain... I pinch my own arm or bite my thumb, slap my hands together or chew my lip.
Used when I am feeling guilty or remorseful about something. Often in use when I am hiding the truth.

- **Read these self-touches and adapt to them.** Back off or perhaps gently probe — you be the judge — when you see soothing or punishing behaviors. Avoid changing things when you see stimulating self-touches... they are an indication that you are on the right conversational track.

- **Do recognize that these self-touches might not be relevant to the actual conversation you are having.** A neck-pinching primary caregiver may be flashing on an earlier argument she had with her boss, even though you see the gesture when you are talking about her father. Try not to jump to conclusions.

- **Jumping to conclusions is dangerous** in any event. While nonverbal behavior does account for 65-95% of the entire message, it is also highly subjective, culturally determined... and easy to misread. When assessing a person's motivations or unspoken thoughts/feelings, look for corroborating evidence... use more than one nonverbal cue and listen to vocal messages when drawing conclusions.

Managing Defensiveness and Conflict

- Remind yourself, and remind your clients, that **venting and anger are normal.**

- **Managing conflict takes energy.** One has to control emotions, listen well and weigh words carefully. The higher you climb toward resolution, the greater your effort.

- Managing conflict is complicated by the fact that different family members are at **different levels of resolution.** For example, a dying man wants to discuss his estate with a daughter who denies that her father is seriously ill.

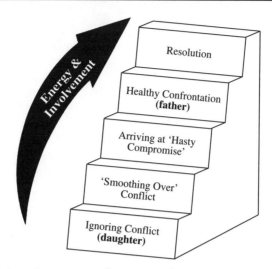

• **There is a Cost–Reward Ratio** in choosing any communication behavior, but particularly in managing conflict. In other words, the rewards have to outweigh the costs, or the confrontation (behavior) won't occur.

$$\text{Behavior} = \frac{\textbf{Reward}}{\textbf{Cost}}$$

Some conflicts are just "not worth arguing about." With others, it seems essential to "lay our cards on the table."

• **It would be easier if everyone agreed on the relative rewards and costs of having a given argument!** For example, in that father-daughter situation, the two people have very different orientations toward the same 'behavior' (discussing the estate).

For the **father**:

$$\text{Discussing Estate} = \frac{\text{Closure, Comfort in Planning/Decisions}}{\text{Energy needed to deal with daughter's resistance}}$$

For the **daughter**:

$$\text{Discussing Estate} = \frac{\text{Pleasing father}}{\text{Facing her own complex emotions, fear}}$$

The father might be so anxious for planning/closure comfort that he is willing to wade through his daughter's resistance. But the daughter's desire to please her father might not outweigh her fears and complex emotions. Thus, the father pushes her to talk about the estate, but the daughter refuses to comply.

• Before we can have a healthy confrontation, **we first have to agree that <u>engaging</u> in the argument will be 'worth it.'**

• **Fifty percent of all people adopt a Flight style when dealing with conflict. Fifty percent of all people adopt a Fight style.**

FLIGHT   Those 'easy-going' people who do not wish to hurt others, sometimes failing to be totally honest.

vs.

FIGHT   Those 'forthright' people who express emotion freely, sometimes without tact or discretion.

• People in primary relationships (husband and wife, mother and son) often have different preferences — theirs is a complementary **Fight-Flight** relationship. Periods of calm and storm — they fight about whether or not they should fight.

• Sometimes, two **Fighters** are in a primary relationship. Theirs is a loud, confrontational method of conflict management. They are energized by argument and they fight about <u>everything</u>.

• Sometimes both parties are **Flight-takers**. Their relationship appears calm but privately, unspoken conflict still exists. They silently wonder if they <u>should</u> fight.

• Fighters accuse Flight-takers of 'stuffing feelings.' Flight-takers accuse Fighters of 'making mountains out of molehills.' **Neither method is better** — they are just different.

• Any time a person has a conflict, s/he **only has a 50% chance of dealing with another person who shares her preference** for Fight or Flight.

• **People in conflict will inevitably behave defensively.**

• **There is no need to apologize for feeling defensive.** Any time we are scared or anxious, we defend and protect ourselves. Defensiveness is normal, and sometimes even helpful.

• **Would you take away the crutches from a person with a broken leg?** Similarly, <u>don't</u> try to "get rid" of a person's defensiveness. We <u>need</u> our defense mechanisms, at least at the moment of anxiety/fear/anger, etc. Instead, be patient. The leg <u>will</u> heal (with a little help) and the crutches won't always be necessary.

• **Rather than <u>denying</u> a person's right to be defensive, learn to recognize specific defense mechanisms.** This will help you to avoid intensifying them:

  The Rationalizer: Finding reasons to justify an unhappy turn of events.

  "It's actually okay that my father is dying… he's old enough to have had a full and happy life."

  Response: Do <u>not</u> discount the explanations/logic of the person, regardless how 'crazy' or 'preposterous'… "It's okay that your father is dying?! Oh, come on now!" This will only make the person 'explain' even more. Instead, just listen, nod… and be sure not to smile (which s/he would certainly find 'patronizing').

The Ostrich: Totally suppressing any feelings of defeat/conflict. Danger lies in the fact that repressed feelings explode, eventually.

"Tina always seemed to be so cheerful and bright, until I found her sobbing hysterically in front of the TV last night. The sound wasn't even turned on. I was really scared... she was the one who was keeping me in control."

Response: Do not try to force the person to 'talk about it'... "Tina, you're in denial — it's so obvious. You'll feel so much better if you just talk about this.' No, she won't... and if you confront her this directly she'll squirm and probably wish she could run from the room. If you feel you must get her to open up, try to ask very neutral, nonthreatening questions. "So, what kind of a day have you had today?"

The Finger-Pointer: Blaming someone else to explain our own fears/failures.

"How can I be expected to put together a decent meal for everyone when I have to spend half the afternoon chasing after your father's prescription?"

Response: Do not try to get the person to accept blame... "Come on now, no one is looking for a gourmet meal and besides, the pharmacy is only 10 minutes away." This will only make the person deny responsibility even more vehemently. Instead say, "It isn't really important how this happened... let's just solve the problem. How about if we order a pizza?"

The Compensator: 'Treating' yourself when things are difficult, threatening, etc.... A basis for serious problems like obesity and chemical dependency.

"The only way I can get through my evening visit to the hospital is to pop over to the mall afterwards. I've bought three pairs of shoes this month."

Response: Do not call attention to the 'treats'... this will not eliminate them; it will only cause the person to hide them. (Obviously in severe cases such as binging, bankruptcy or alcoholism, intervention is sometimes necessary.)

The Protestor: Publicly taking a position that is the opposite of what you privately feel, because you think your private thoughts are wrong or taboo.

"Why should anyone be afraid of dying? We've always believed that God has a better future in store for us!"

Response: Like the Rationalizer, this person will only become more defensive if you point out inconsistencies and illogical statements. Avoid arguing and don't focus on what was said; let the statements slide.

The Reactor: Taking out anger or frustrations on something unrelated to the conflict — hopefully an inanimate object, but not always.

"Boy, Rita was really slamming the dishes around last night!"

Response: Do not tell the person to "calm down"... this will only infuriate him/her even more. Instead, get out of the way! Later, calmly acknowledge apologies and try not to make the person feel any more guilty about damage that was done... allow them some private time to clean up, repair and replace. (Obviously in severe cases of physical/verbal abuse, intervention is in order.)

The Passive-Aggressor: Acting as if nothing is wrong, but secretly planning on 'revenge,' and often to be carried out later.

"Paul has been so charming, even funny lately. Then last night he told me he wouldn't be coming by once a week anymore. I wanted to talk to him about it, but he kept denying anything was wrong."

Response: This is one of the more 'slippery' mechanisms because often the 'aggression' won't occur until days, weeks or even months after the triggering event... so it is harder to see a connection. It's best to try to find the connection yourself... then directly address the aggression and mention a possible triggering event. "It seems like our relationship has changed... does this have anything to do with that remark I made about your sister?" Unfortunately, you won't always receive a truthful answer, so you might remain confused. But sometimes just acknowledging the aggression/triggering event is enough to make the behavior stop.

• **Do not immediately argue with a defensive person.**
Contradicting him will make him even more defensive. Instead, use Nonevaluative Feedback Techniques (see pages 37-38).

• **The best way to manage defensiveness is to expect it, acknowledge it, and avoid intensifying it.**

NOTES

The Visit

- **Call the family before your visit to confirm;** this builds trust and spares inconvenience. For instance, imagine that a patient is unexpectedly hospitalized... if the family knows the hospice worker phones before visits, there is one less responsibility on their shoulders.

- **Confirming phone calls also provide an additional opportunity to talk with patients and especially primary caregivers...** not only will you be more prepared for the next visit, but in a private phone call the caregiver might be more willing to share those fears/feelings that are harder to discuss face-to-face, in the presence of the patient.

- **Bring something to do** on the visit (a good book, letters to write) for those times the family prefers to be left alone.

- **Things to bring in your hospice bag:** book, magazine, stationery and pen, gloves, lotion for hand massages, handiwork, a snack, a journal, playing cards, tissues, emergency info…

- **Things to do on a hospice visit:** give the patient a manicure, make-up, write letters for patient, read to patient, massage, bathroom/kitchen tidying, walk the dog, grocery shopping, pharmacy pick-up, errands, provide transport to appointments, 'chum' with the patient (cards, lunch, talk, country drives, look at old photographs, share hobbies, etc.).

- **Most important thing to do on a hospice visit:** know when the client wants to be left alone.

- **Let the family control your visit.** When you arrive, ask: "What needs to be done today?"

- If the family doesn't seem to know what to do with you, **suggest something.** "Can I do a load of wash?" "Would a massage help?"

- Remember that **'keeping out of the way'** is sometimes the best thing you can do.

- A lot of hospice care consists of **how ingenious you can be** in helping families solve their problems… from physical therapy issues like drinking from a glass to logistical issues like scheduling to emotional issues like reconciliations.

- **Be creative. Also be wary** of 'getting in over your head' — be prepared to offer referrals.

- **Ask questions** of other team members when you have concerns.

- **Leave notes, share information** with other team members when you find something that works.

- **Each team member brings a unique perspective to the case, and each leaves a personal imprint with the family.**

NOTES

Taking Care of Yourself

- **Pat yourself on the back for communicating at the very highest level** possible. (It requires tremendous skill and energy to ask the right questions, create trust, mediate, monitor airtime, read between the lines, reduce defensiveness... all simultaneously!)

- **Engage in stress-release activities:** exercise, journal writing, humor, hobbies, family rituals and traditions, eating well, rest, meditation, massage, outings with friends, spiritual nurturing, relaxation tapes, music therapy, imagery exercises, bereavement support groups, storytelling, etc.

- **Hospice workers need respite, too.** Let your team members know when you need some time and distance.

- **Avoid judging or second-guessing your own reactions when patients die.** Crying profusely isn't necessarily 'over-involvement,' feelings of numbness don't necessarily mean that you are 'uncaring' or 'burnt out.'

- **Do not permit your own family and friends to put you on a pedestal because you are a hospice caregiver:** "You of all people should be strong enough to handle this... after all, you work with dying people!"

- **Don't worry about making mistakes.** I don't know of a caregiver in the world (even one with decades of experience) who can't think of a time when she wishes she'd said or done something differently.

- **Avoid feeling anxious even if it seems you are 'doing nothing.'** In essence, you cannot change this family, and you cannot change their circumstance. Your contribution is not what you <u>do</u>, but just that you are <u>there</u>.

- **Many times, it may seem as if you don't make a difference. But you do.**

NOTES

Resources

ORGANIZATIONS

- National Hospice Organization (NHO)
  1901 North Moore Street, Suite 901
  Arlington, VA 22209
  703/243-5900

  Through reasonable membership and meaningful mailings, one has access to hospice periodicals, conference notices, video resources, books, support services, etc.

- Joining your state hospice organization is an excellent way to network and keep current on regional resources, workshops and support.

MAGAZINES/PERIODICALS

- *Hospice Magazine, Journal of Psychosocial Oncology, Journal of Palliative Care, Thanatos, The Hospice Journal, American Journal of Hospice Care.*

ELECTRONIC SEARCH

Use your community and college library databanks to obtain articles/books/multimedia from your area libraries. Categories might be: hospice, homecare, death, dying, bereavement, grief, palliative care, pain management, cancer, oncology, AIDS, terminal illness, family systems, conflict, neurolinguistics, personality, nonverbal communication, body language, etc.

BOOKS

There are far too many to list. Here is just a sample:

Beissler, Arnold R. **A GRACEFUL PASSAGE: Notes On The Freedom To Live or Die** Doubleday, NY, 1990
Essays and personal reflections on living and the right to die, how and when one chooses. The author's earlier book, FLYING WITHOUT WINGS, tells the story of his learning to live a passionate and meaningful life after being stricken with polio and paralyzed at age 25.

Callanan, Maggie and Patricia Kelley **FINAL GIFTS: Understanding The Special Awareness, Needs And Communications Of The Dying** Poseidon Press, NY, 1992
This beautifully written book was produced by two experienced hospice nurses who describe the theory they call 'Nearing Death Awareness.' Through their own work and through discussions with peers, they discovered that while much of the final communication we receive from a dying person appears incoherent or confusing, it is actually a poignant and often symbolic attempt to describe the dying experience. Callanan and Kelley discovered that the dying person's messages are frequently metaphorical, and that those messages typically fall into one of two main categories: a description of the actual dying experience, and requests for something the person needs in order to have a peaceful passing. The authors tune us into the universal symbols and metaphors that often appear in a dying person's communication and they offer us advice for listening, deciphering, and responding. In other words, if we listen correctly, we are rewarded by extremely powerful information about what it is like to die, and we are also better equipped to provide for any special needs the dying person might have.

Carroll, David **LIVING WITH DYING: A Loving Guide For Family And Close Friends** Paragon House, NY, 1991
This is a helpful, reader-friendly book which contains some good insights and more depth than many books in the 'self-help' genre. The author uses a question/answer format to discuss lots of issues and ideas, under these chapter headings: talking with the dying about death, coming to terms with death: stages of acceptance, the experience of dying, caring for the dying, the rights of the patient, how children view death, caring for the dying child, home care, sources of help, the hospice, an appropriate death, practical preparations, bereavement, living with AIDS, and references/books of general interest.

Colgrove, Melba with Harold H. Bloomfield and Peter MacWilliams
HOW TO SURVIVE THE LOSS OF A LOVE Prelude Press,
1991
A psychologist, physician, and poet/songwriter team up to produce this best-selling self-help approach to grief (over 2 million copies in print). The book begins with a helpful few chapters defining loss, then offers 94 'points' — ideas, insights, and action plans. An accompanying workbook contains exercises and space for personal reflection: SURVIVING, HEALING AND GROWING: THE WORKBOOK Prelude Press, 1991. The authors also offer an audio tape version of their work.

Davies, Phyllis **GRIEF: Climb Toward Understanding** Carol
Communications, NY, 1988
The author's personal reflections, letters and poetry on experiencing the loss of her 13 year old son, Derek, in an airplane accident. It is especially helpful in that she also compares her thoughts and feelings to those of her husband, her surviving daughter, Derek's friends, and others who have been touched by his life and death. The last quarter of her book contains practical checklists for dealing with morticians, the funeral, holidays, living wills, memorials and ideas for commemoration, plus resource lists of helpful organizations. Interspersed are lovely drawings and lots of room for a reader to journal, draw, make notes, etc.

Duda, Deborah **COMING HOME: A Guide to Dying at Home
with Dignity** Aurora Press, New York, NY 1987
If I had to choose just one book to read and recommend to patients, their loved ones, and hospice workers, this would be it. Written with sensitivity and graceful dignity, Duda begins her book by describing her personal involvement with three very different at-home deaths — those of her father and two close friends. She continues to provide a wealth of information about all facets of the dying process; she covers physical, legal, psychological, spiritual issues, and much more. What I like best about this book is Duda's holistic approach (with some extremely creative and surprising advice), plus her tone (which is completely free of judgment and marked by 'unconditional' acceptance).

James, John W. and Frank Cherry **THE GRIEF RECOVERY
HANDBOOK: A Step By Step Program For Moving Beyond
Loss** Perennial Library, 1989
The authors are co-founders of the Grief Recovery Network; this book contains thoughtful essays and psychological insights about loss and grief… and a few exercises.

Karnes, Barbara **GONE FROM MY SIGHT: The Dying
Experience**, available for $3.00 from Barbara Karnes, P.O. Box
335, Stillwell, KS 66085
A pithy little pamphlet that outlines the physical and mental changes that occur as death approaches, from 1-3 months, 1-2 weeks, days, hours and minutes. While sometimes given to families by their hospice programs, it is important to note that death doesn't necessarily progress in such a 'clock work' fashion.

Keirsey, David and Marilyn Bates **PLEASE UNDERSTAND ME: Character and Temperament Types** Prometheus Nemesis Book Company, Del Mar, CA, 1984
This classic best seller is probably the best existing introduction to the famous 'Myers-Briggs Type Indicator' test. Written for the layperson, the book begins with a questionnaire so that readers can discover their own personality types. The authors continue with an indepth description of the types, their similarities and differences, and the potential difficulties that arise when people interact with personalities that are 'too' different — and 'too' similar! — to their own. The authors' theme is acceptance rather than change... as Keirsey is quoted on the back cover, "It's okay to marry your opposite and beget children who are far from being chips off the old block, but it is not okay to take marriage and parentage as a license to SCULPT spouse and child using yourself as a pattern to copy. PUT DOWN YOUR CHISEL. LET BE. APPRECIATE."
In my workshops, I cover the Myers-Briggs model... participants tell me it illuminates their personal relationships as much as it helps them better understand and work with their hospice clients.

Kübler-Ross, Elisabeth
Perhaps the most highly renowned — and controversial — expert on death and dying, Kübler-Ross is also a prolific writer on the subject. Beginning in the 60's with ON DEATH AND DYING and more recently publishing AIDS: The Ultimate Challenge, she has also written:
QUESTIONS AND ANSWERS ON DEATH AND DYING
TO LIVE UNTIL WE SAY GOODBYE
LIVING WITH DEATH AND DYING
REMEMBER THE SECRET
DEATH: THE FINAL STAGE OF GROWTH
ON CHILDREN AND DEATH
WORKING IT THROUGH
Though I have yet to read all her works, I am struck how unique each is. From photo portraits and poignant interviews to clinical descriptions of death and bereavement, each book has been written to speak to a distinct audience. Her voice is penetrating and wide-reaching.

Morgan, Ernest with editor Jenifer Morgan **DEALING CREATIVELY WITH DEATH: A Manual Of Death Education And Simple Burial** Celo Press, NC 1988
This classic is fabulously informative and completely pragmatic about many aspects of dying, and particularly those things which families might be concerned about but are too embarrassed/shy/nervous to discuss. Chapter headings include death education, living with dying, bereavement, the right to die, simple burial, memorial societies, death ceremonies, and how the dead can help the living. The 'appendix' is over one-third of the entire book and contains extremely practical information — bibliography, support groups, financial support, living wills, anatomical gifts, hospice organizations and much more. There is even a section on how to build a simple burial box. Written with sensitivity coupled with direct honesty, this book is endorsed by both Elisabeth Kübler-Ross and Jessica Mitford. Inexpensive and immensely informative... worth the shelf space.

Osis, Karl and Erlendur Haraldsson **AT THE HOUR OF DEATH** Hastings House Book Publishers, Mamaroneck, NY, 1990
A clinical overview of the death experience: deathbed visions, apparitions, depression and pain, back from death experiences. Good source citation.

Sankar, Andrea **DYING AT HOME: A Family Guide For Caregiving** The Johns Hopkins University Press, NY, 1991
A well-written and practical book which offers thoughtful insights and advice on the entire process of dying at home, from making the decision to after the funeral service. Based on interviews with dying people, their loved ones and professional caregivers. Chapter headings include taking the patient home to die, strangers in the home: the use of formal support, caregiving, social support, the well-being of the caregiver, demystifying death, and after death. The 'appendix' covers the typical... living wills, nursing homes, resources, etc., but this book provides something others do not — a 30-page appendix on "Tasks and Problems of the Caregiver," covering physical care and concerns an untrained family member or hospice volunteer might have, such as hygiene, sexuality, nutrition, elimination, transfers, agitation, administering medications, cognitive impairment, etc. Very helpful to a medical novice.

Sarton, May **A RECKONING** W.W. Norton Company, NY, 1978
A poignant novel which traces the final year of Laura Spellman, who is diagnosed with inoperable lung cancer and chooses to die at home. Through this process, she comes to terms with the relationships she has with her family and friends, but her most essential relationship becomes the one she develops with her nurse, Mary.

MOST IMPORTANT RESOURCE

- Collect the personal 'stories' most people are willing to share about their own experiences with death and dying. Pay particular attention to learning the rituals and customs of other cultures.

About the Author

M. Catherine Ray, McRay Company, has offered communications training since 1977. She holds an MA in Speech-Communication and a BA Magna Cum Laude in Interpersonal Communication. Recently, she attended the Postgraduate Institute of Psychosocial Oncology at Memorial Sloan-Kettering Cancer Center, New York City.

Catherine is on the faculty at Metropolitan State University, where she was honored by students with the 1991 'Excellence in Teaching Award.' She teaches Interpersonal Communication, Negotiation, and Public Speaking. While in graduate school she taught at the University of Minnesota and College of St. Thomas.

Since 1985, Catherine has specialized in hospice training; she provides volunteer and team management training for a sizable percentage of the hospice programs in Minnesota. During the winter months she offers workshops in warmer climates.

Catherine's article *"Smart Talk"* appeared in the Spring 1991 issue of *HOSPICE Magazine*. She is a hospice volunteer at Methodist Hospital Hospice, Minneapolis.

ORDER FORM

Please send me _____ copies of *I'm Here To Help.*

Name _____

Hospice/Affiliation _____

Address _____

City _____ State _____ Zip _____

☐   Check here if you would like to receive workshop information.

Price <u>includes</u> shipping and handling anywhere in the U.S.
Please allow 3 weeks.

# Copies	Price
1-49	$7.00
50-99	$6.50
100-249	$6.00
250+	$5.50

Copies _____ X Price _____ = $_____
Your Total
Payment

To keep down costs, we respectfully request payment prior to
shipping. Please make your check or money order payable to
McRay Company and mail to:

HOSPICE HANDOUTS
McRay Company
780 North Arm Drive
Mound, Minnesota 55364

612-475-4003

**We encourage you to distribute *I'm Here to Help*
at your local inservices and conferences.**

Cut along dotted line

Do you know anyone else who might be interested in *I'm Here to Help?*

Name _____

Hospice/Affiliation _____

Address _____

City_____ State_____ Zip _____

Name _____

Hospice/Affiliation _____

Address _____

City_____ State_____ Zip _____

Your comments are appreciated: